Design draw

John Rolfe The Mayflower School, Billericay

HODDER AND STOUGHTON
LONDON SYDNEY AUCKLAND TORONTO

Preface

Graphic communication is playing an ever increasing part in the school curriculum. Graphicacy is taking its rightful place alongside literacy and numeracy as a form of expression and understanding. This book, along with its predecessors *Design Drawing One* and *Two*, shows the extremely important part that this form of communication plays in our lives. One only has to pick up a newspaper and look through it to see just how much information is presented to us in graphic form.

As the subject becomes more recognized so more examinations are being offered in graphic communication and the examples in the *Design Drawing* series will help prepare students for the type of work required for these examinations. You will find that many of the examples in this series of books require students to undertake research and produce original designs and solutions to various problems. I feel that learning should be enjoyable and to this end I have related the examples used in these books to things which young people are interested in and which they come into contact with in their everyday lives. I have developed a series of themes to try to show how drawings can be based on almost any topic and not just engineering as has so often happened in the past with technical drawing. Although the book is aimed mainly at a graphic communication course there are many examples which could fit into a more traditional technical drawing course.

A number of the examples included in this book require the use of squared paper, a drawing medium which, in my opinion, is very much under used in schools. It can enable students to produce drawings quickly and accurately without a great deal of costly equipment. Another extremely useful drawing method is also explored: that of using a square grid to enlarge and draw quite complicated objects which would be almost impossible using more conventional techniques. Architectural drawing also seems to be forming part of a number of examination courses and a section of the book is devoted to this.

Colour, shading and texturing must play an important part in the type of work dealt with in this book and I hope that students will be given the opportunity to explore as many different mediums as possible. Students will have already experienced coloured pencils and felt tip pens (both excellent mediums when used correctly) but try also things like gummed and coloured paper, sticky-back plastic and perhaps even the air brush. In a book of this type it is difficult to go into detail about colour but I have shown a few techniques which can be used as far as shading and texturing is concerned. Study the photographs in the book, they will help you to pick out light and dark areas, highlights, textures etc.

Don't be afraid to try out ideas, they may not all work but I'm sure that most will help to improve the presentation of your work and make it more alive and interesting. I hope you enjoy the book and the ideas it contains.

John Rolfe

Acknowledgements

The author and publisher would like to thank the following organisations who have allowed their trade or other marks to be used in this book, or who have supplied photographs. In all cases the dimensions and methods of construction of the symbols are the responsibility of the author, and not necessarily those employed by the organisations, whose co-operation in this respect is appreciated.

Royal Navy (Exercise 2); British and Irish Steam Packet Company (U.K.) Limited (3); Townsend Thoresen (4); B.A.S.F., E.M.I. Records U.K. The C.B.S. logo is a trademark of C.B.S. Inc. and is used with their permission. Brian Long (6); E.M.I. Records U.K. (7); Wallace Arnold Tours Ltd (9); Roadline (10); R.A.C. (11); British Road Services Ltd (12); London Express News and Feature Services, Sporting Pictures (U.K.) Limited (13); London Express News and Feature Services, Morley Pecker (14); Mark Shearman (15); London Express News and Feature Services (16 and 17); Stoke Evening Sentinel (18); Mitre Sports (19); West Ham United Football Co. Ltd (20); Dunlop Sports Co. Ltd (21); The Commonwealth Games Federation (22); The Tesco Group of Companies (23); Distributive Industry Training Board (24); Gateway Building Society (25); Granada Motorway Services (26); The Birmingham Post and Mail Ltd (27); Brian Long (28); Shell International Petroleum Co. Ltd (29); Entam Leisure Ltd (30); Kawasaki Motors (U.K.) Ltd (31); Heron Suzuki GB Ltd (32); B.S.A. Co. Ltd (33); Alitalia Linee Aeree Italiane SpA (34); British Airports Authority (35); British Airways, Manchester International Airport Authority (36); Saudi Arabian Airlines Corporation (37); Alexander Duckham and Co. Ltd, BL Cars (38); Ford Motor Co. Ltd (39); Elf Aquitane U.K. (Holdings) Ltd (40); The Colt Car Co. Ltd (41); London Weekend Television, Yorkshire Television Ltd (42); United Artists Corporation Ltd (43).

1: Sailing dinghies

A series of sail markings from various craft are shown.

a) Make a series of drawings of them. Use a piece of A4 5 mm squared paper for your work.

b) The dinghy chosen for the main drawing is an International Flying Dutchman. The Flying Dutchman originated in Holland in 1951. She has now developed into one of the premier two man racing dinghies in the world and has been used in every Olympic Games since 1960. Make a drawing of the dinghy on a piece of A3 paper using a grid of 15 mm squares.

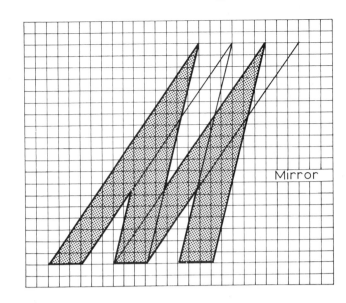

Mirror

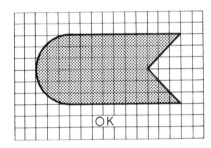

OK

Albacore

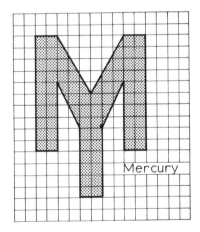

Mercury

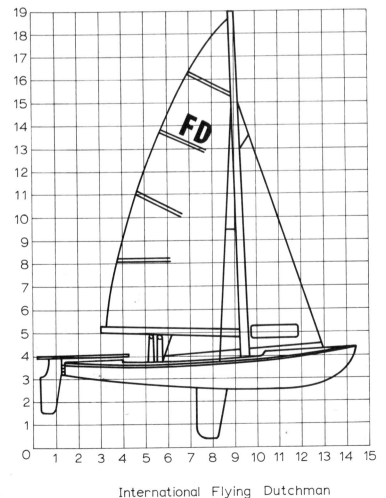

International Flying Dutchman

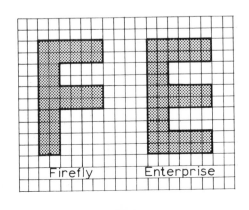

Firefly   Enterprise

2: Royal Navy

a) Make a drawing of the linked letters shown here. Use a piece of A4 5 mm squared paper for your drawing.

b) The series of smaller drawings show various naval ranks. See if you can find out the rank depicted in each drawing. Make a further series of drawings to show other naval ranks.

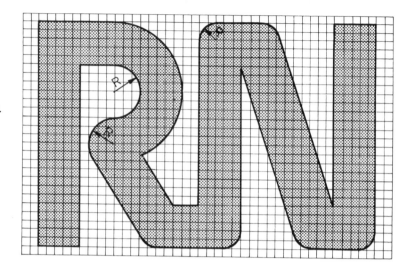

■ Blue

ROYAL NAVY

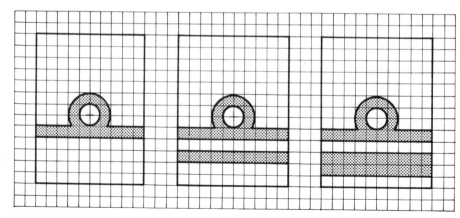

■ Yellow

c) There are many different classes of ships in service with the Royal Navy. See if you can make a list of these different classes. The one chosen for the drawing here is H.M.S. Amazon, a type 21 anti-submarine frigate. H.M.S. Amazon was commissioned in 1973. Defensive armament includes Seacat anti-aircraft missiles, a fully automatic 4.5 in Vickers Mk 8 gun, a Wesland Lynx helicopter armed with air to surface missiles and homing torpedoes.

In order to make a copy of the drawing of H.M.S. Amazon first draw a grid of 30 squares by 10 squares, each square having a length of 13 mm. You will find that this grid will fit on to a piece of A3 drawing paper. Once you have drawn the grid you can transfer the outline and details of the ship square by square until you have completed what should be an accurate drawing of H.M.S. Amazon. You can use this same drawing technique to make a drawing from a photograph. Find a photograph of another Royal Navy ship, draw a grid over the photograph and make a drawing of it.

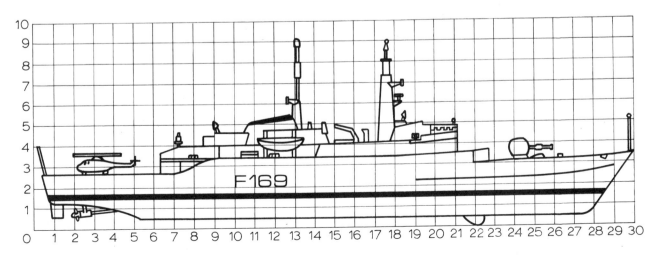

H.M.S. Amazon

3: B and I Line

What type of craft do this shipping line operate? See if you can collect any photographs of these craft. What routes do they operate on?

a) The main drawing shows the insignia used by the B and I Line. Notice how the letters have been given a three dimensional appearance. What do we call this type of drawing? Make a drawing of the letters on a piece of A4 5 mm squared paper. What do the letters B and I stand for?

b) Also shown is a drawing of the Plimsol Line. What is it and why is it marked on the side of ships? Make a drawing of the Plimsol Line on a piece of A4 5 mm squared paper.

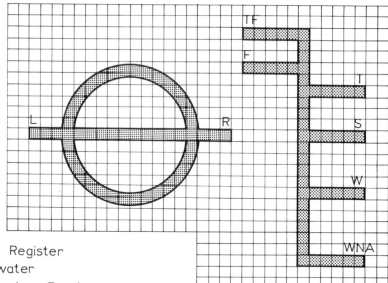

LR	Lloyds Register
F	Freshwater
TF	Freshwater Tropics
T	Saltwater Tropics
S	Saltwater Summer
W	Saltwater Winter
WNA	Winter North Atlantic

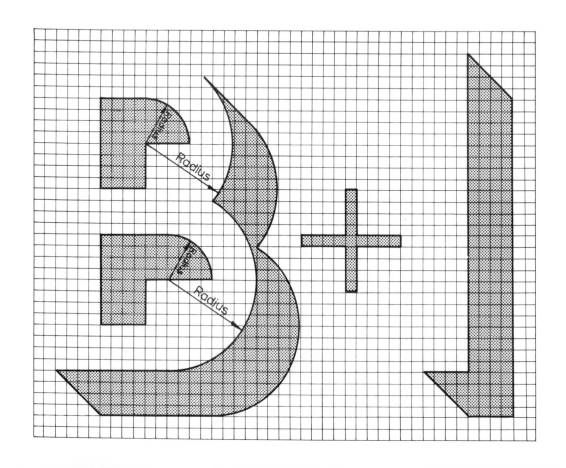

4: Townsend Thoresen Ferries

See if you can find out what routes this shipping company operate on. Visit a travel agent and see if you can obtain a booklet which will give you the information. Make a series of diagrams to show the routes operated.

   The drawing shows the company's insignia which links together the initials T. T. F. Can you pick out these letters in the design? Where is this insignia usually shown on the boat? Make a drawing of the Townsend Thoresen Ferries insignia on a piece of A4 5 mm squared paper.

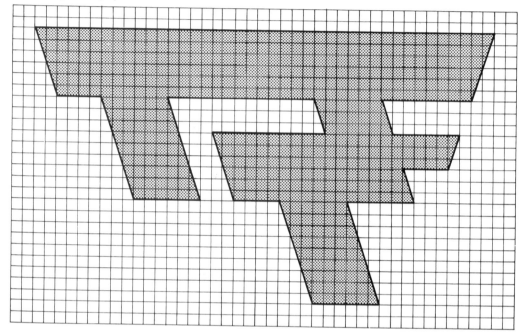

□ Orange

5: Lettering styles

The names of many of today's recording artists
lend themselves very well to this piece of work.
The aim is to produce a piece of lettering which
suggests the meaning of the word, hence we
have Kate Bush in letters shaped like bushes,
Boney M with letters formed out of bones and
The Shadows with a shadow underneath.

   Which is your favourite group or artist? Does
the name lend itself to a piece of lettering like the
examples shown? If so see what sort of ideas you
can think of.

6: Record and tape labels

All of the major record and tape labels have their own logo. Have a look at the Top Ten and see if you can find out what logo each of the records has. Try to think what each of the logos means, does it contain the initials of the company? Does it have a design or picture rather than letters? Which of the logos do you think is the best? Make a collection of record label logos and see if you can make drawings of some of them. Draw the logos shown.

Why not try designing your own recording label? Think of a suitable name and design a logo for it. Perhaps you could organise a competition with some of your friends to see who can produce the best design.

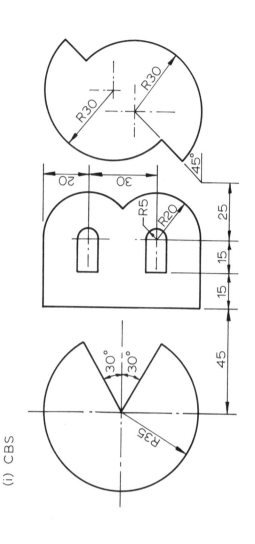

(i) CBS

(ii) EMI

Red

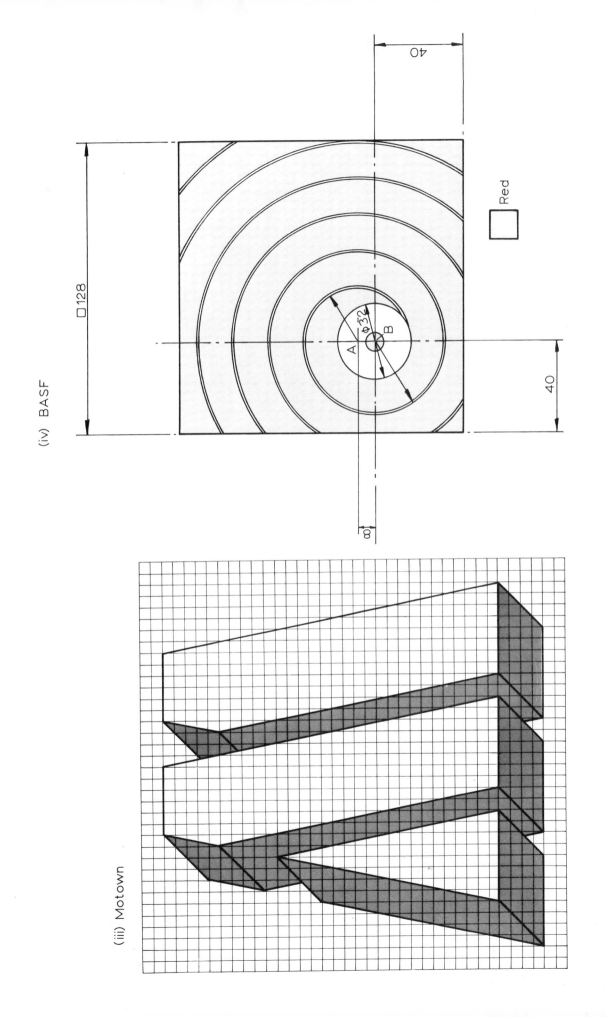

(iv) BASF

□128

40

40

Φ32

A

B

8

Red

(iii) Motown

7: Block graph — Chart entries

Information about the sales and success of records can be recorded in a number of ways, the best known of these is the top 75 charts which are produced for both single and L.P. records and are published each week.

The example shown here uses information based on the number of entries in the L.P. charts by various recording artists. It uses columns to represent numbers of hit long playing records and it is very easy to compare one recording artist's success against another.

a) Make a drawing of the block graph which is shown. Use your drawing to answer the following questions.
   (i) How many hit singles did Status Quo have in this period?
   (ii) Were groups or single artists the most successful hit makers during this period?

Four pie charts have been used here to compare the make up of the Top Twenty over a period of fifteen years. What major change can you see? In these examples each record is represented by an angle of 18°.

a) Draw these pie charts and use them to answer the following questions.
   i) How many male groups were there in the February 1967 chart?
   ii) Which chart contains the most male/female groups?
   iii) Which do these charts seem to indicate are more popular, single artists or groups?

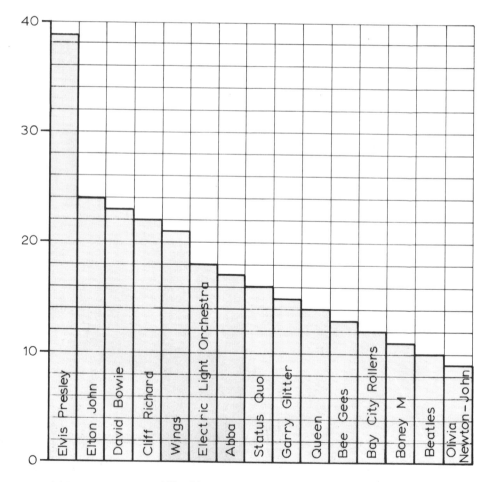

Hit Singles 1970–1980

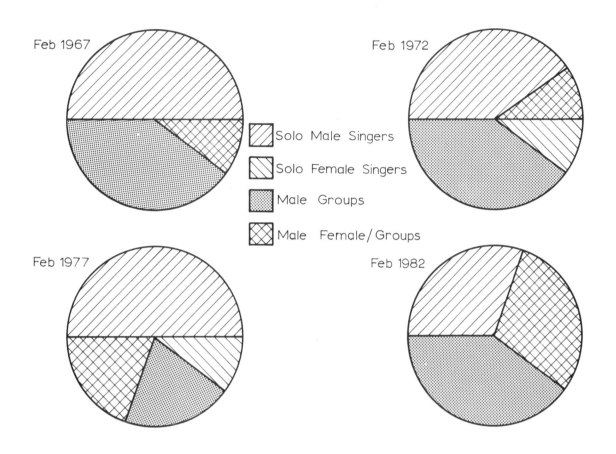

Feb 1967

Feb 1972

Solo Male Singers

Solo Female Singers

Male Groups

Male Female / Groups

Feb 1977

Feb 1982

8: Flow chart – History of The Shadows

What is your favourite pop group? I like the Shadows and I have tried to trace the history of the group from around 1956 until the mid 1960's by using a flow chart. By using such a chart it is fairly easy to see how and when each member came to join the group and what happened to those that left. Originally called the Drifters, The Shadows saw several changes in personnel but two members have remained even to this day. Hank Marvin, lead guitar and Bruce Welch rhythm guitar. See if you can find out who the other members in the present line up of The Shadows are. Perhaps you could produce a similar type of chart for your favourite pop group.

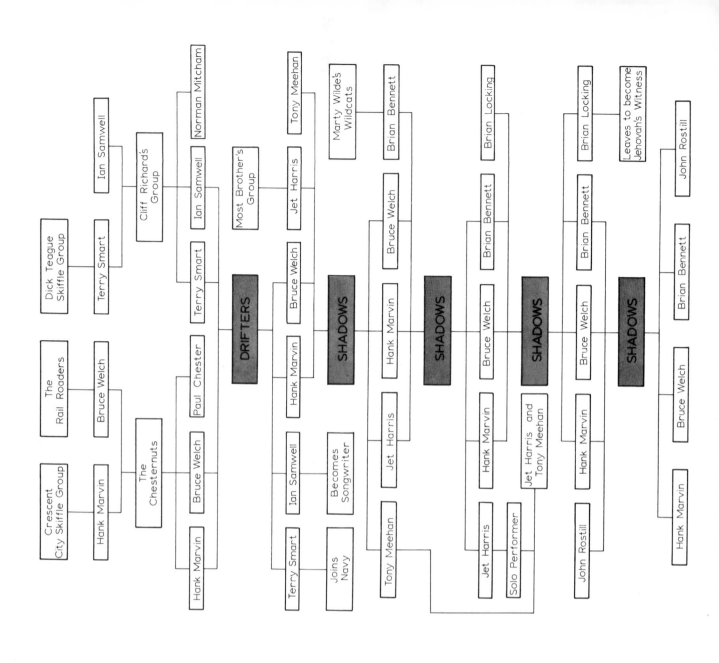

9: Wallace Arnold

The insignia used by Wallace Arnold cleverly links together the letters W and A. Using a 15 mm grid make a drawing of the coach shown below. Details of how to draw the Wallace Arnold insignia are also shown. By using a suitable size of grid add this insignia to your drawing. Finally add any lettering which you think necessary and colour your drawing.

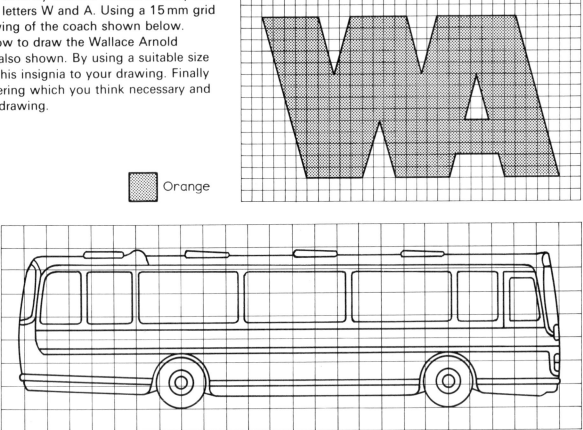

▨ Orange

10: Roadline

What sort of service do Roadline operate? What does this logo which is carried on the side of their lorries communicate to you?

a) Make a drawing of the Roadline logo.

b) The series of smaller drawings show various road signs which are in common use. Find out what each of them means. Make accurate drawings (approximately the same size as the Roadline logo) of two other road signs.

c) The three dimensional drawing is of a Fiat lorry. Make a copy of this drawing on a 15 mm square grid. Make a collection of lorry photographs and perhaps try drawing some of them.

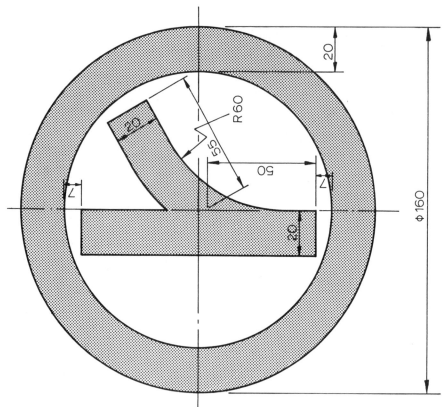

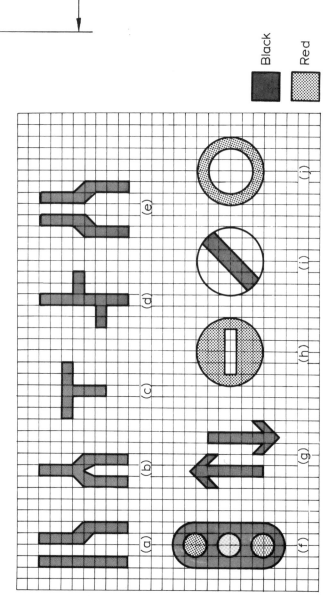

Black ⬛   Orange ▨

Red ▧   Green ▨

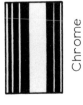

Chrome

Glass

Textures

Try to use these textures on your drawing

Fiat 159 F20T

11: Royal Automobile Club

This drawing shows the lettering on the present day R.A.C. badge.

a) Make a drawing of the complete badge, including the background shape and the crown, on a piece of A4 5 mm squared paper.

b) The second drawing shows a Ford Transit Van which is to form part of the R.A.C. fleet. Make a copy of this drawing on a 15 mm square grid. Once you have completed the drawing add the R.A.C. logo and any suitable lettering to the drawing. Finally colour the drawing in the R.A.C. colours of blue and white.

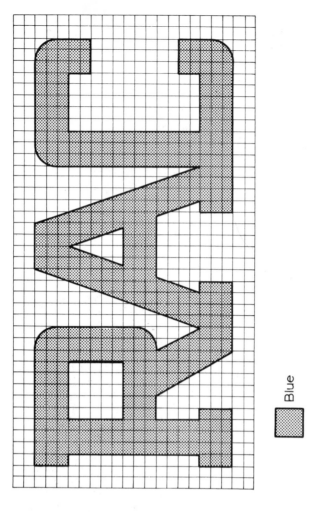

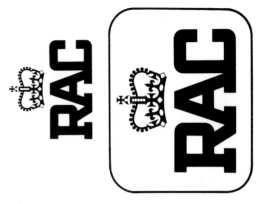

☐ Blue

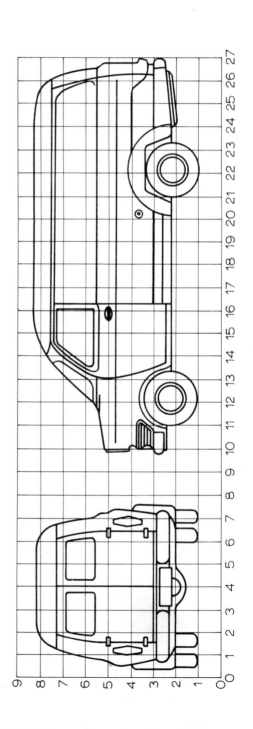

When you come to colour your work answer these questions :-

   (i) Where are the light and dark areas ?

   (ii) How will be best to colour the wheels ?

   (iii) How can you represent the windows ?

12: British Road Services

What does the B. R. S. design opposite communicate to you?

a) On a piece of A4 5 mm squared paper make a drawing of this logo.

b) The route plan which is drawn here shows how it is possible to produce a drawing which gives very clear information and is much easier to follow than the more conventional form of map. It is the type of drawing which would be useful for a lorry driver to carry in his cab as it only requires a quick glance to tell if the correct route is being followed.

Either. (i) To a suitable scale make a copy of the route plan which is shown here.

or (ii) Take two towns which are approximately 50 miles apart and produce a similar type of route plan for the journey between the two towns.

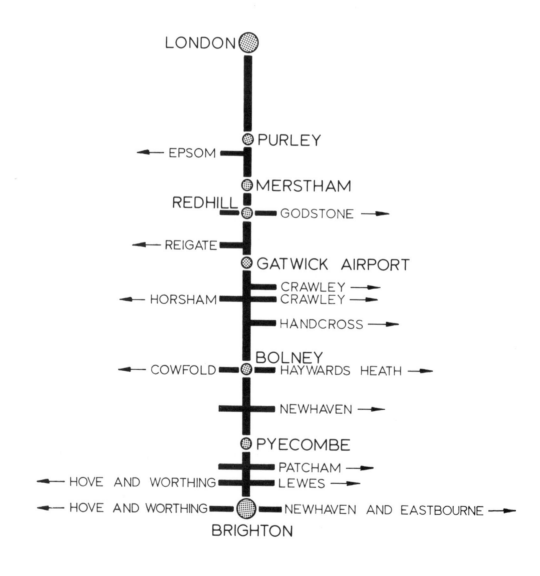

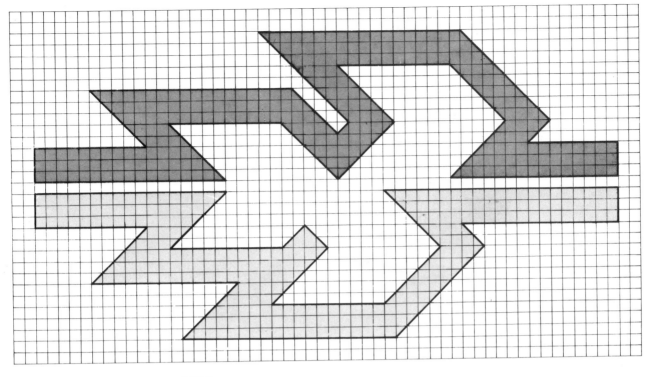

Red

Blue

13: Athletics stadium

The series of drawings show a running track and the areas needed for various other athletic events. On a piece of A3 paper draw the running track to a scale of 2 mm to 1 metre. The areas for the other events are to be marked out inside the running track. Plan a suitable layout for these areas and mark them in on your drawing. Make a list of the other facilities you think should be provided at a major athletics stadium. Add these other facilities to your drawing.

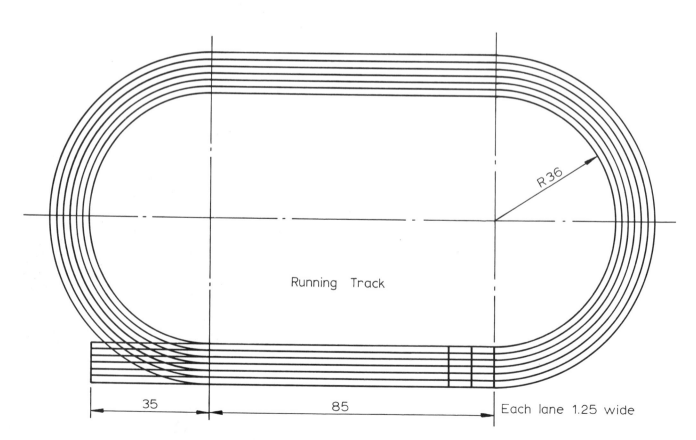

Running Track

R 36

35

85

Each lane 1.25 wide

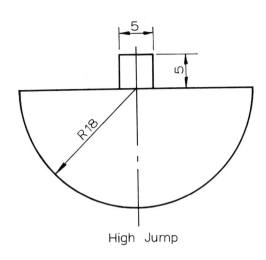

High Jump

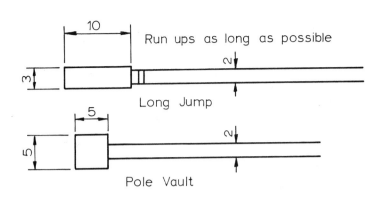

Long Jump

Pole Vault

Javelin

All dimensions are in metres

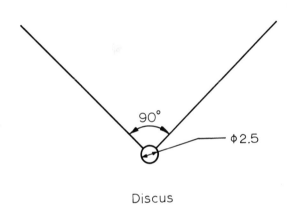

Discus

Shot

14: Sports field

The groundsman of a sports club is faced with the problem of marking out the following pitches on a piece of ground, a plan of which is shown.

a) Three association football pitches.
b) Two rugby football pitches.
c) Two hockey pitches.

How would you solve the problem?

Using a scale of 1 mm to 1 metre make a drawing of the piece of land on a piece of A2 paper. Mark in on your drawing the changing rooms, the car park and the trees (these are not to be cut down). Cut out pieces of card or paper to represent the various pitches and move them around on your plan until you find suitable positions for each of them. When you have decided upon a suitable layout for the area draw in the various pitches on your plan.

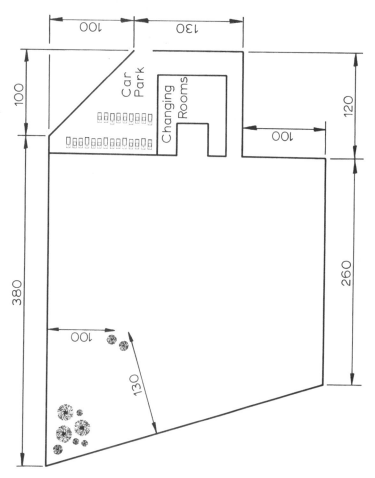

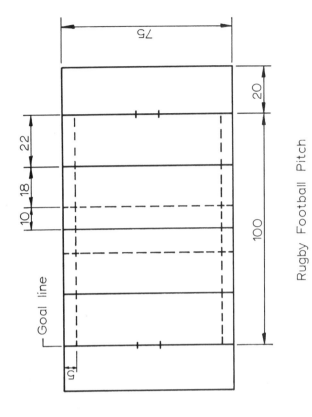

Rugby Football Pitch

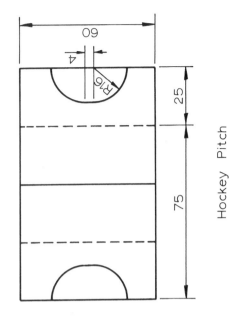

Hockey Pitch

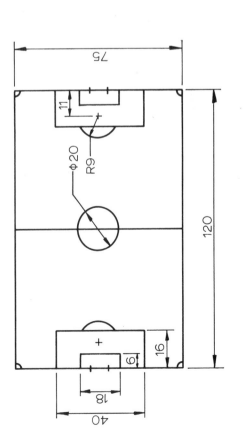

Association Football Pitch

15: Sports hall

The drawing shows the plan of a sports hall. Among the activities to take place in the hall are basketball and badminton and the floor has to be marked out for a basketball court and four badminton courts. The badminton courts will have to be marked out over the basketball court. What problems will this cause and how could you overcome them? To a scale of 10 mm to 1 metre draw a plan of the sports hall and mark in the various courts in the positions that you think would be most suitable. What other games could be played in a sports hall? Make a list of those that you can think of and from this choose one and mark out a court for it on your sports hall plan.

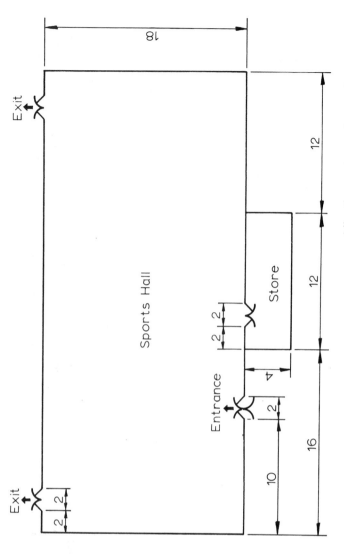

Exit

Exit

2 2

Sports Hall

Entrance

Store

2 2

2

4

10

16

12

12

18

All dimensions in metres

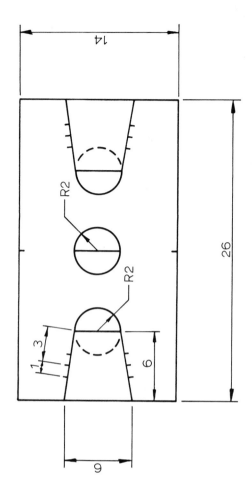

R2

R2

3

1

6

6

9

14

26

Basketball Court

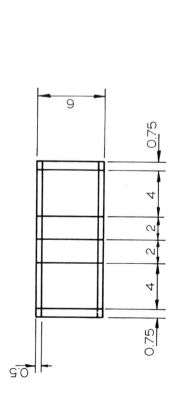

6

0.75

4

2

2

4

0.75

0.5

Badminton Court

16: Flow chart – F.A. Cup

The flow chart shown here involves the various football teams in a knockout cup competition. Spaces have been provided to record the teams and results from the quarter finals through to the eventual winners of the competition. Using the last F.A. Cup as the basis of your work draw out the boxes shown on to a piece of 5 mm squared paper and enter the terms and results in the appropriate spaces.

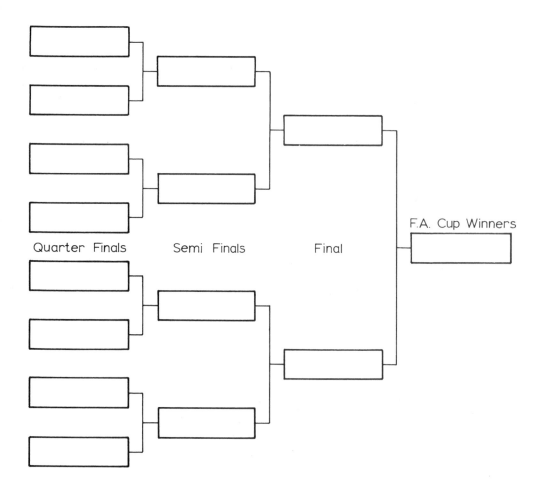

Quarter Finals   Semi Finals   Final   F.A. Cup Winners

17: Snooker

Have you ever played snooker? How many balls are used in a game of snooker?

a) Two snookers are shown in the drawings. What is a snooker? In example (i) the centre of the white ball is 5 mm from the top of the table and in the centre of the table. The ball to be hit is 20 mm from the bottom of the table and 10 mm from the right hand side. Using this and other information given in the drawing plot the path that the white ball would follow. Do the same for example (ii). In this the white ball is 5 mm from the left hand side of the table. The ball to be hit is 8 mm from the right hand side and 35 mm from the bottom of the table.

b) Make a drawing of a snooker table with the balls in the positions they would be in at the start of a game.

c) The second drawing shows all the red balls in the triangle which is used to arrange them at the start of a game. Using the information given make a drawing of the triangle and the fifteen red balls. How big is each side of the triangle?

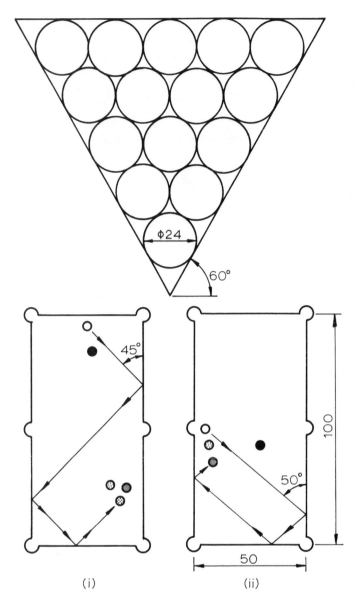

(i) (ii)

18: Dartboard

Darts is a very popular game, do you play?

a) Using the following information make a drawing of the dartboard shown here. The drawing consists of circles of the following diameters 5, 12, 80, 88, 132, 140, 176 and 198 mm. Add the numbers 1–20 in their correct positions around the board.

b) The smaller drawing on squared paper shows a design for a dart. Make a copy of this design and then design three other shapes which you think would be suitable for darts.

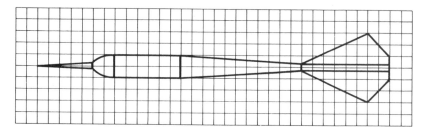

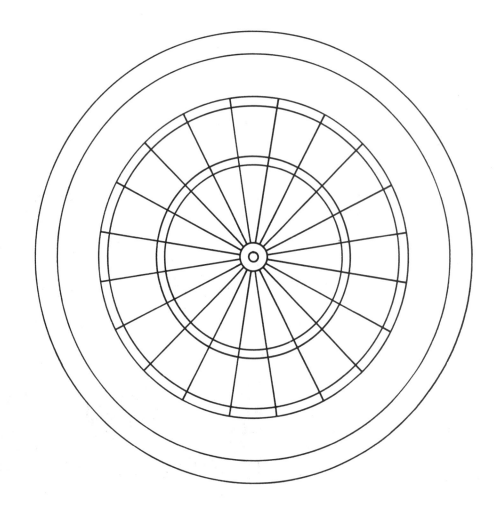

19: Football

Shown is a stylised drawing of a football. Can
you think of anywhere that you have seen a
design of this type?

a) Make a copy of this drawing. Start with the
   pentagon in the centre and work out.

b) The smaller drawing on squared paper
   represents the shirt, shorts and socks of a
   footballer. It is designed to be the basis of
   your next piece of work. Make a series of
   drawings similar to the one shown. Colour
   each one in using the colours of some of your
   favourite football teams.

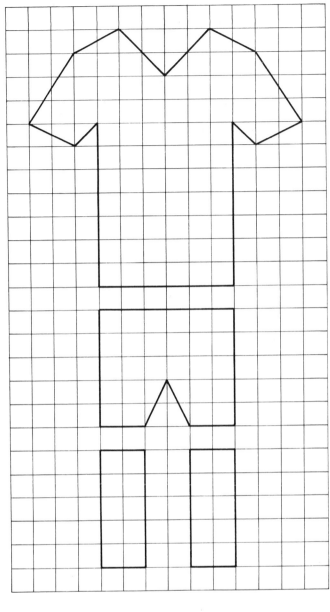

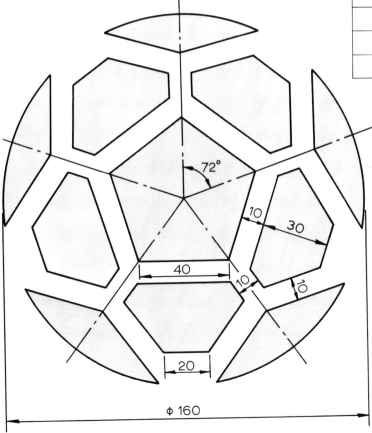

20: West Ham United

Why are West Ham United known as the
'Hammers'? If you look at the drawing of the club
badge you will see the 'Hammers'. What is the
rest of the badge based on and why?
Make a drawing of West Ham United's club
badge on a piece of A4 5 mm squared paper.

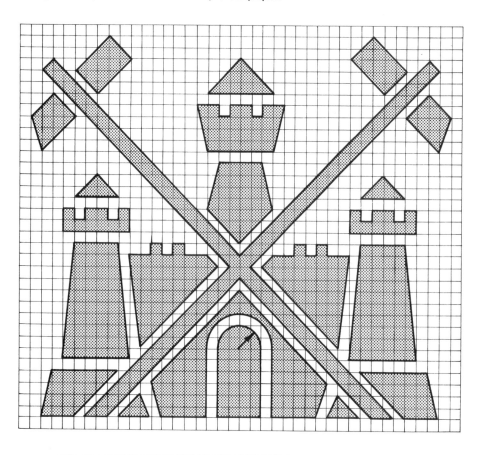

21: Dunlop

Dunlop manufacture a wide range of products including many items of sports goods. The drawing shown here is based on a tennis racket onto the strings of which is to be printed the Dunlop trademark.

a) Using the given drawing as the basis of your work make a drawing of a complete tennis racket including the strings. Show on your drawing how the Dunlop trademark would look when printed onto the strings.

b) Find out the markings and size of a tennis court and make an accurate scale drawing of it.

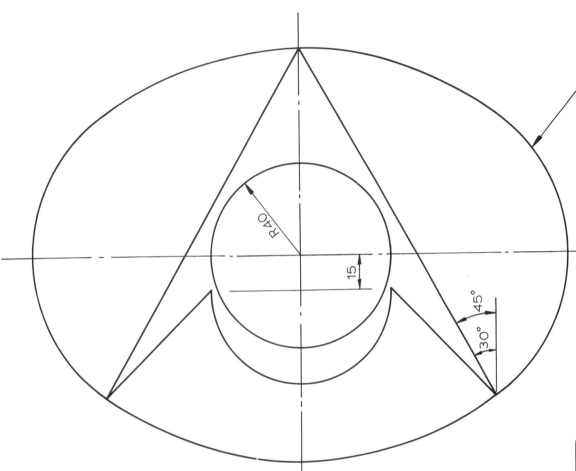

R40

15

30° 45°

Ellipse major axis 240
minor axis 150

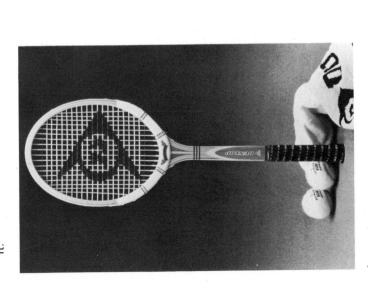

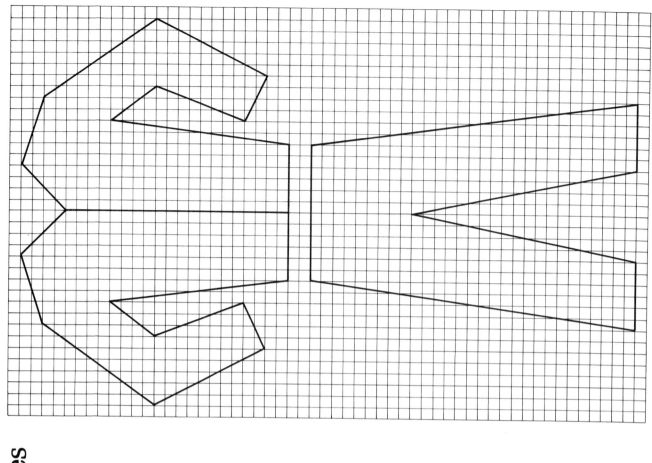

22: Edmonton Commonwealth Games

The 1978 Commonwealth Games were held in Edmonton, Canada. The symbol used at those games is drawn here. What do you think the design is based on?

a) Make a drawing of the 1978 Commonwealth Games symbol.

b) Design a track suit for your country's team to wear at a major athletics meeting. On a piece of A4 5mm squared paper draw the basic outline of a track suit which is shown and add to this outline in order to produce a design which you think would be suitable for the team to wear.

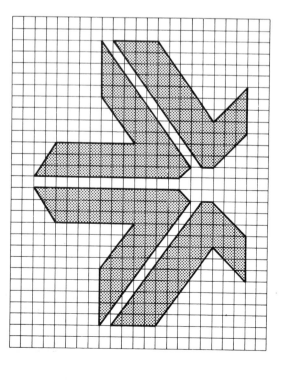

Edmonton 1978

XI Commonwealth Games
August 3rd to 12th

XIe Jeux du Commonwealth
du 3 au 12 août

23: Supermarket cash desks

The exit area of a supermarket is shown. Into this area are to be placed six cash desks the size and shape of which is also given. Make a drawing of the area and plan out suitable positions for the cash desks. Remember that you must have space for making a queue at each desk and access for supermarket trollies (the size of which is 1 m x 0.5 m) You will find it a help if you use cardboard cutouts for the cash desks and trollies to plan the area. You can try various arrangements before you decide upon the most suitable and then make your final drawing.

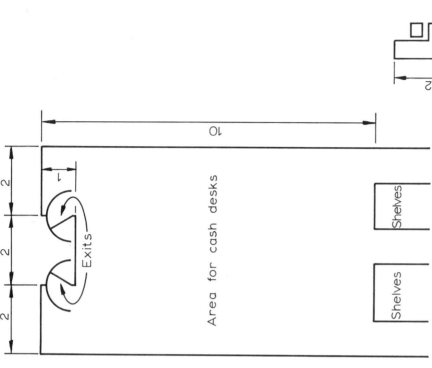

Exits

10

2 2 2 2

1

Area for cash desks

Shelves   Shelves

All dimensions are in metres

Cash Desks

2

1

24: Award for Staff Training

This award is given to shops which operate a training scheme for their staff. What do you interpret the design as being?

a) Make a drawing of the award. What do we call this type of three dimensional drawing?

b) When a large order for a big London department store arrived it was contained in boxes and crates which had the symbols shown here marked on the outside. What do you think each of the symbols mean? Make drawings of two of the symbols and then devise a symbol to show that a crate contains livestock.

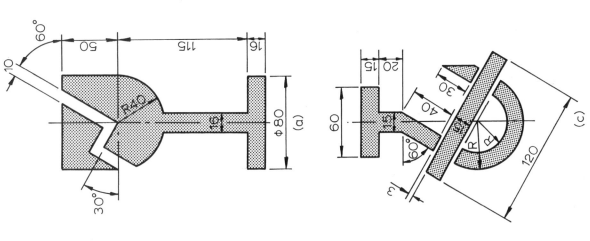

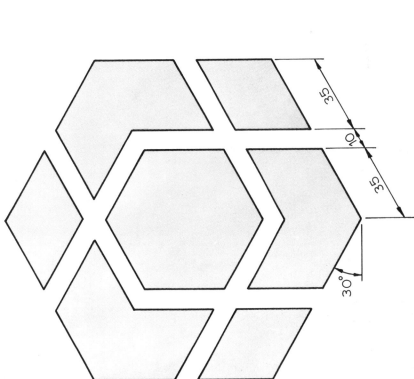

25: Gateway Building Society

The Gateway is only one of the many Building Societies in this country. The logo that it used is one which has a double meaning, can you see what they both are? Make a drawing of the sign on a piece of A4 5 mm squared paper.

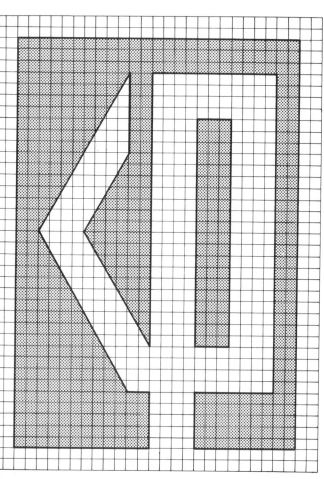

Red

26: Motorway service area

The drawing shows a section of motorway, the areas each side of which are to be developed as service areas. The facilities to be provided are as follows:

a) Garages on each side of the motorway.
b) Parking on both sides of the motorway.
c) Restaurant.
d) Toilets.
e) Shop.
f) Footbridge to link both sides of the motorway.
g) Slip roads to leave and rejoin motorway.
h) Picnic Area.

Draw to a suitable scale such a development. Plan your work by listing sizes and making sketches before you start on an accurate drawing of the area.

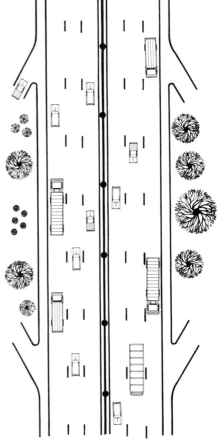

27: Road junction

One road crosses over another as shown in the drawing. Design a road junction which would enable the following flow of traffic to take place.

a) Traffic from A to join C
b) Traffic from D to join A
c) Traffic from B to join D
d) Traffic from C to join B

Make an accurate drawing of your design using a scale of 10mm to 1 metre.

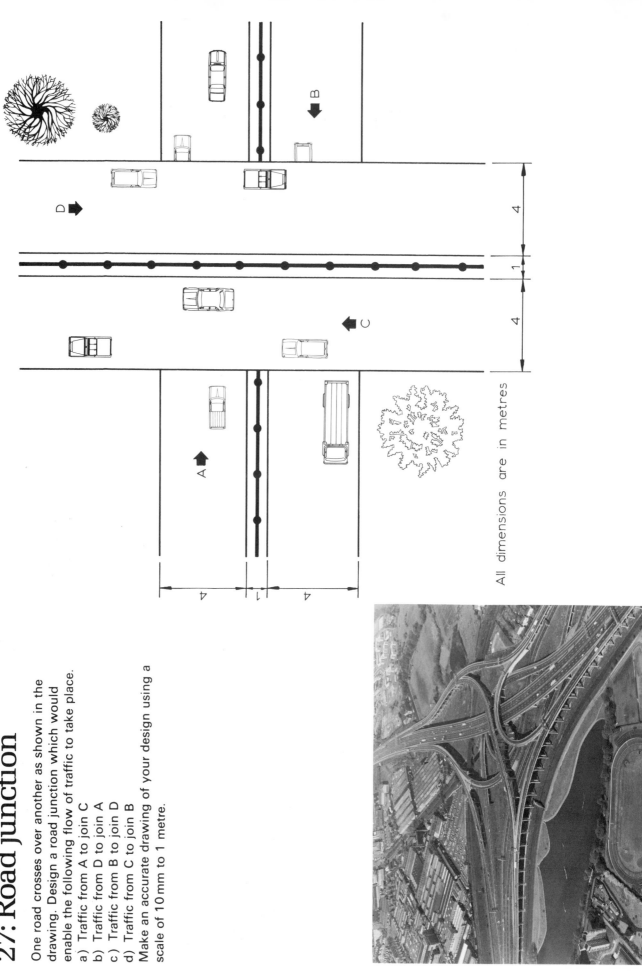

All dimensions are in metres

28: Car park

The area of land shown in the drawing is to be developed as a car park. In addition to parking spaces, toilets are to be built. Lines 2.5 metres apart are to be drawn to define parking spaces and each parking space must be 5 metres long. A gap of 5 metres must be left between each row of parking spaces to allow for easy entry and exit of cars. To a scale of 10mm to 1 metre make a drawing of the car park and mark in the parking spaces and the toilets in the positions which you think would be the most suitable.

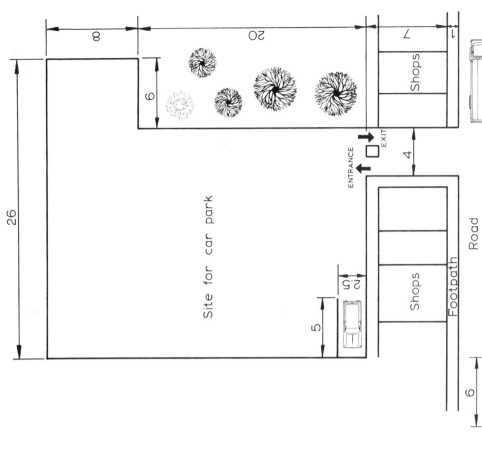

Site for car park

Shops

Footpath

Road

Shops

Toilet Block

All dimensions are in metres

29: Service station

The area of land in the drawing is to be developed as a service station. Among the facilities to be provided are the following, all sizes are in metres:

a) Car wash 10 × 5
b) 4 petrol pumps each 1 × 0·75
c) Repair shop 12 × 8
d) Sales area 15 × 5
e) Cash desk 3 × 2
f) Office 3 × 7
g) Toilets, each 2 × 2

Draw the site to a scale of 10 mm to 1 metre. Make card cutouts of each of the items to be built on the site, use these to help you plan out the most suitable positions for each of the buildings. You should also check for access for cars, this can be done by making another cutout to represent a car and by moving this around your plan. Take the size of an average car as being 4·5 × 1·7 metres. When you have achieved what you think to be a successful solution to the problem draw the various buildings in on your site plan. Add any other facilities which you think a service station should provide and which you have room for on your site.

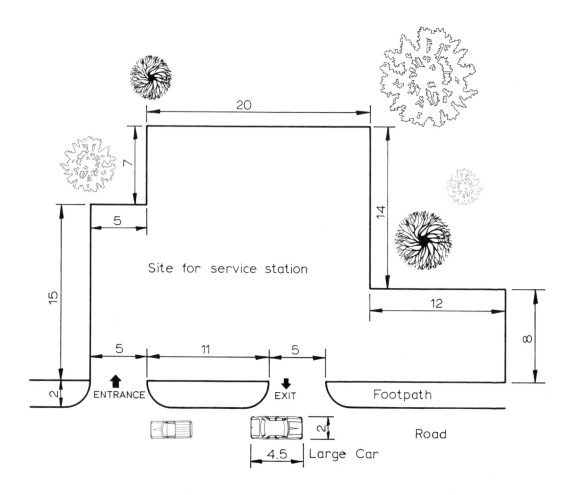

30: Belle Vue Speedway Club

Where is Belle Vue Speedway club based? See if you can find out why their club badge is based on the ace of clubs.
a) Make a drawing of the club badge.
b) Have a look at the drawing of a Speedway motorbike. How does it differ from the type of motorbikes you see on the roads? Make a copy of the Speedway bike on a grid of 20 mm squares. Add any other pieces of detail to your drawing which you think would improve the appearance of the motorbike.

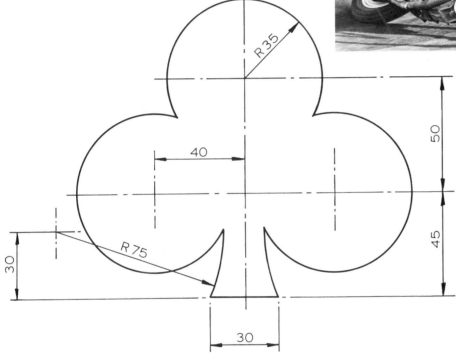

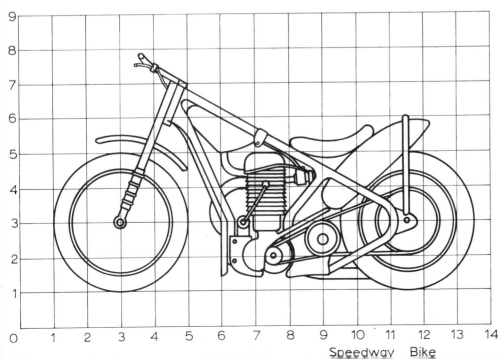

Speedway Bike

31: Kawasaki

What type of motorbikes do Kawasaki manufacture? Where is the company based? See if you can collect some photographs of motorbikes made by them.

a) Make a drawing of the Kawasaki logo. Take particular care when drawing the four part ellipses.

b) The Kawasaki KE 125 is perhaps the most complicated drawing in the book. Make a copy of the drawing on a grid of 10 mm squares. It will probably take you a long time to complete but with care you should be able to produce a very accurate drawing.

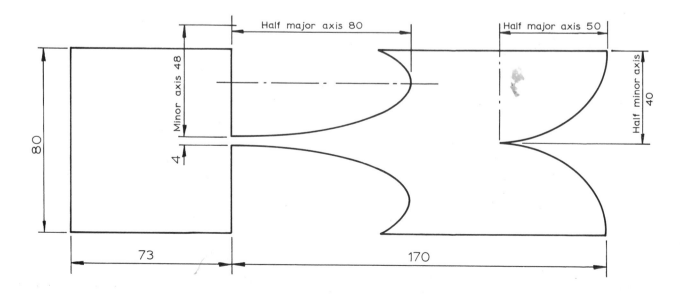

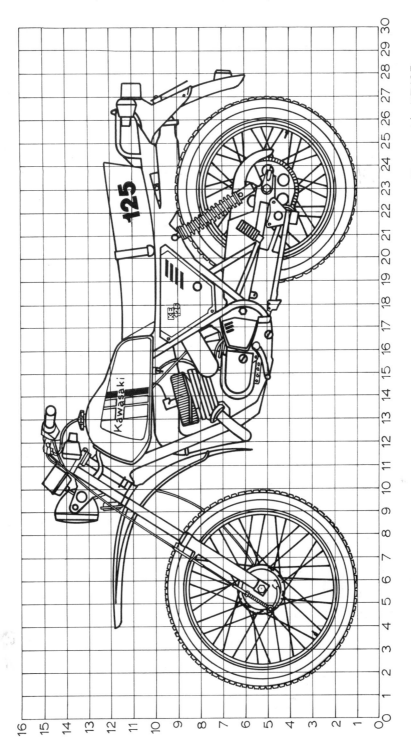

Kawasaki KE125

32: Suzuki

See if you can find out any information about Suzuki motorbikes. Why do you think Japanese motorbikes are so popular in this country?

a) Make a drawing of the Suzuki S
b) The second drawing shows a motorbike fairing. What is a fairing and why are they fitted to some motorbikes? Make a copy of the fairing.

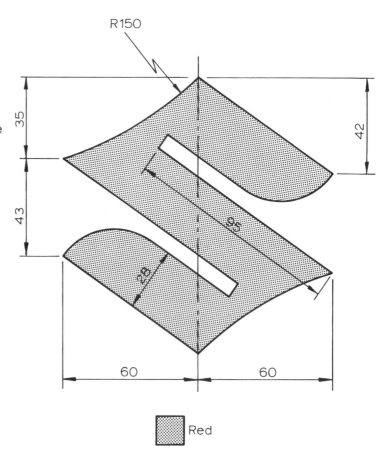

R150

35

43

42

60   60

□ Red

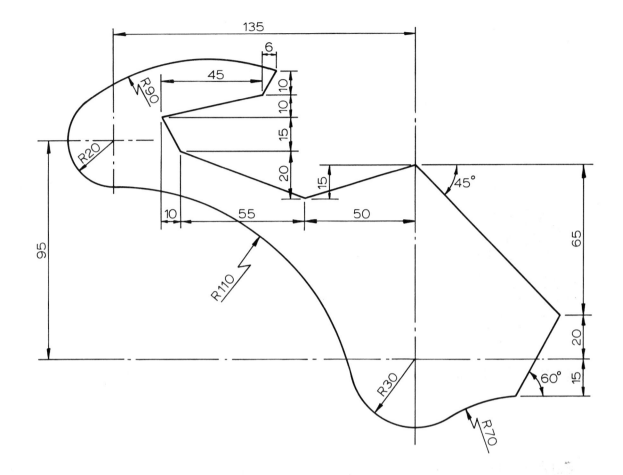

33: Perspective lettering: B.S.A.

What do the letters B.S.A. stand for? What are
B.S.A. most famous for producing?

a) Follow the stages shown here to draw the
   piece of lettering. Colour your drawing in two
   tones of the same colour to achieve the same
   effect as that shown in the drawing.

b) Use the piece of lettering that you have drawn
   as the basis of a poster advertising one of
   B.S.A.'s motorbikes.

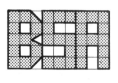

Stage 1

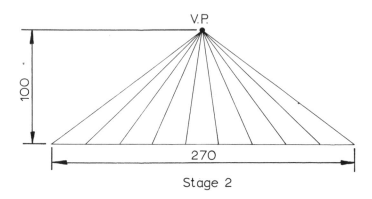

Stage 2

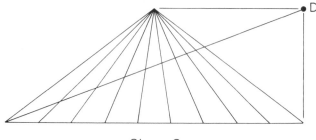

Stage 3

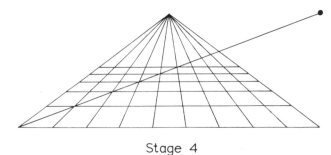

Stage 4

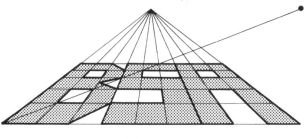

Stage 5

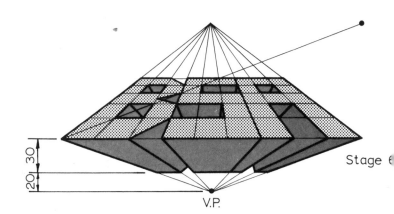

Stage 6

Use transparent coloured sticky back plastic
on your finished drawing. Use one layer all
over and a second layer where you want
a darker tone.

34: Alitalia

Alitalia is the national airline of which country?
What do you think their insignia represents?

a) Make a drawing of the Alitalia insignia.
b) One of the aircraft flown by Alitalia is the DC
   10. On a grid of 15 mm squares make a copy
   of the DC 10 drawing shown here. Add the
   Alitalia insignia and colour scheme to your
   drawing.

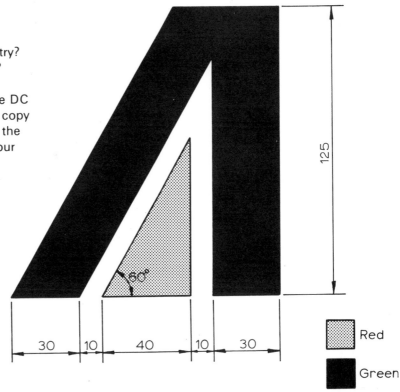

125

30   10   40   10   30

60°

▨ Red

■ Green

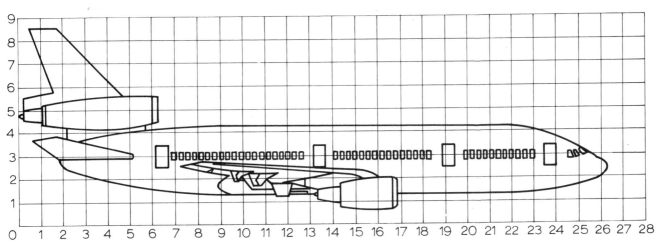

9
8
7
6
5
4
3
2
1
0   1 2 3 4 5 6 7 8 9 10 11 12 13 14 15 16 17 18 19 20 21 22 23 24 25 26 27 28

DC 10

35: Airport passenger lounge

The drawing shows the outline shape of an area
which is to be used for a passenger lounge at an
airport. Make a drawing of this area to a scale of
10 mm to 1 metre. This main area is to be divided
up to provide the following facilities.
a) A Bar.
b) Six booking in desks
c) Toilets
d) Customs area
e) A bookstall
f) A restaurant
g) An area for sitting
h) Offices
Decide upon a suitable size for each of the above
items and then draw them in suitable positions on
your plan. Include walls, doors, windows and any
other details you think necessary.

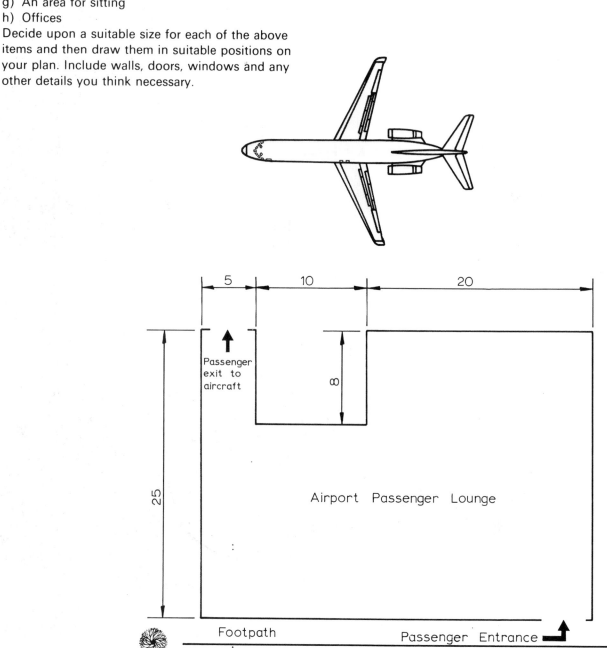

Airport Passenger Lounge

Passenger exit to aircraft

Footpath

Passenger Entrance

Road

All dimensions are in metres

36: British Airways

How do you think the British Airways insignia was arrived at?

a) Make a drawing of the British Airways insignia

b) To help an aircraft pilot manoeuvre his aircraft when it is on the ground a Marshaller or 'Batman' is used. At all airports Marshallers use the signals shown here: (i) Move ahead (ii) Turn left (iii) Start engines (iv) Move into this bay (v) Slow down (vi) Cut engines on side indicated.

In order to make these signals clear the Marshallers use two orange bats or two lights. Turn the following descriptions into drawings of the type shown here.

To tell the pilot to stop the Marshaller raises both bats above his head and crosses them over several times.

To tell the pilot to slow down an engine the Marshaller stands with one bat by his side and the other bat is raised and lowered with an outstretched arm.

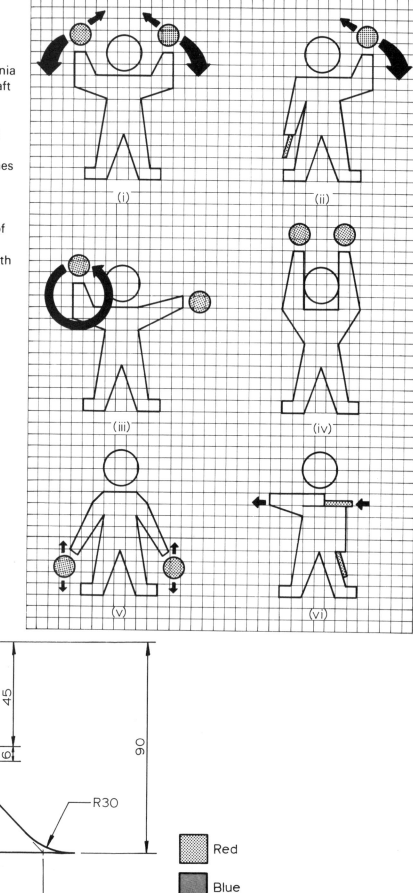

Red

Blue

37: Saudia Leyland Williams

This piece of work is based around the successful Formula 1 racing car, the Saudia Williams FW 07.

a) When did the Williams first appear on the Grand Prix circuit? On a piece of A4 5 mm squared paper make a copy of the word Saudia. Where does this word appear on the car?

b) Draw a grid of 15 mm squares and make a drawing of the Williams car. Add to your drawing the sponsorship markings that the car carries when racing.

c) Why do racing cars have aerofoils? Make drawings of the two aerofoil shapes shown and add sponsorship markings of your own choice.

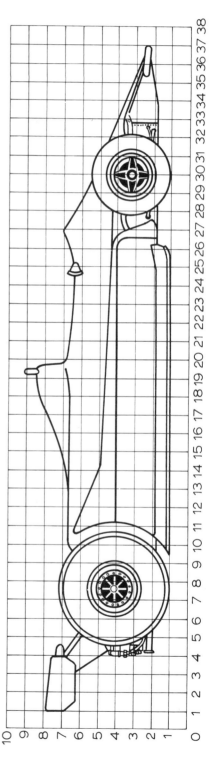

Saudia Williams FW07

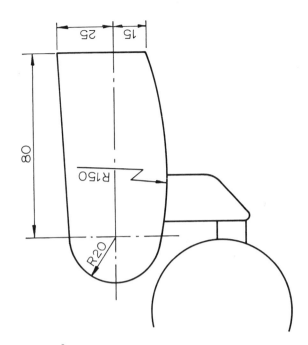

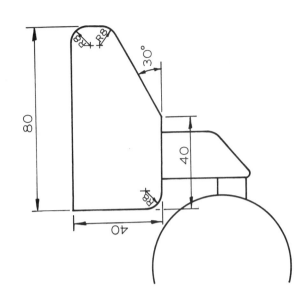

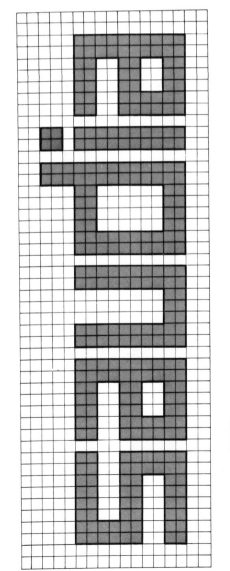

Green

38: Duckhams Motor Oil

a) This drawing shows the letter Q which forms
the Duckham logo. As part of an advertising
campaign it has been suggested that
Duckhams should have a lapel badge which
could be given away to customers buying
their oil. The basis of the badge is to be the
letter Q which is shown here. See what ideas
you can come up with for such a badge and
make an accurate drawing of your best idea.

b) Copy the drawing of the Triumph TR7. It has
been drawn on a squared grid to help you.
Make a drawing of the car on a grid of 15 mm
squares. Add sponsorship markings for
Duckhams. Note that the photograph shows
the TR7 coupé.

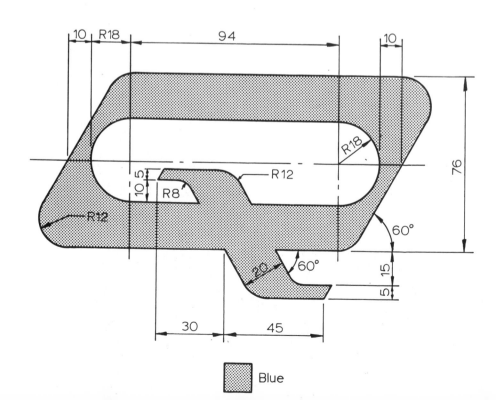

Blue

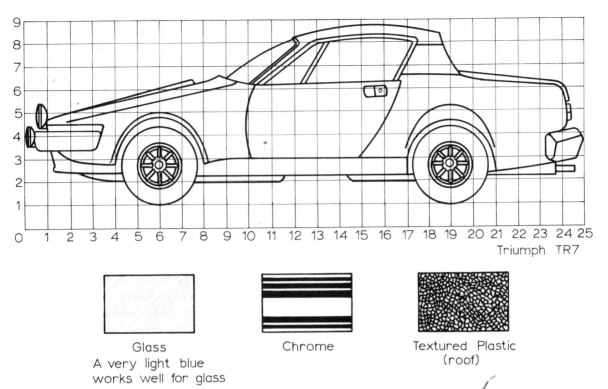

Triumph TR7

Glass
A very light blue
works well for glass

Chrome

Textured Plastic
(roof)

Try these textures on your finished drawing. Remember to use light and dark tones.

VAC 361 X

39: Ford

The Ford logo uses an ellipse as its background shape.

a) Make a drawing of the logo including the lettering.

b) Now look at the drawing of the Ford Escort. As you can see the car has been drawn on a grid of squares. Draw a similar but enlarged (20 mm) grid. By transferring the outline and details of the car square by square you will find that you can make a very accurate drawing of the car. See if you can get hold of any picture or drawings of other Ford cars and make drawings of them in the same way as you have with the Escort.

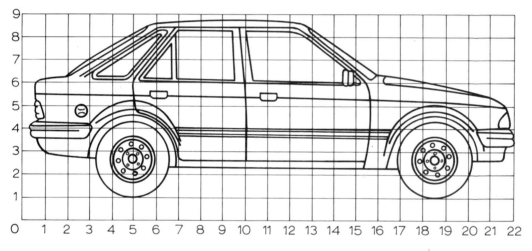

Ford Escort

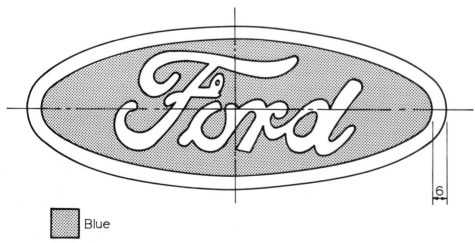

Blue

Ellipse major axis 175
minor axis 60

Outer curve is parallel to ellipse

40: Elf

The drawings below show the outline of a racing driver's helmet and the symbol used by the Elf petrol company. Elf are to sponsor a racing car and their symbol is to be used on the helmet of the car's driver. On a piece of A4 5mm squared paper make a drawing of the helmet with the Elf logo placed somewhere on it. Add any other details which you think would improve the appearance of the helmet. This could be in the form of stripes or other markings in the same colours as the company's logo, blue and red.

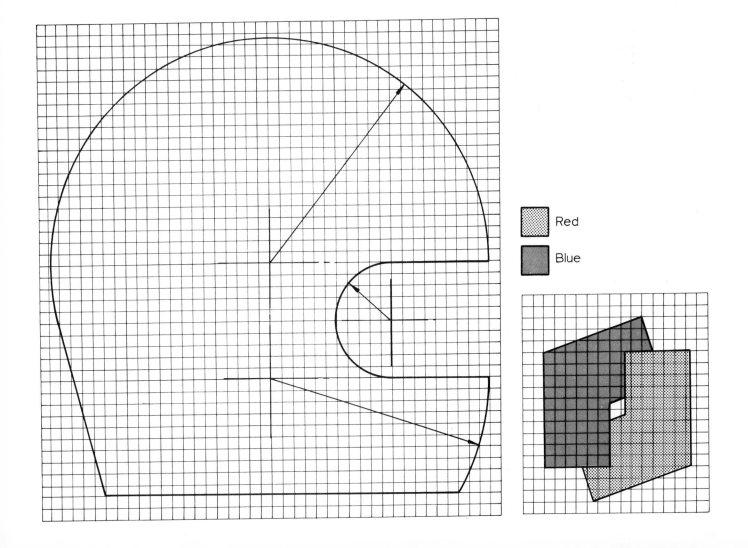

Red

Blue

41: Colt

Where is the firm that makes Colt cars based?
What other makes of car come from this same
country?

a) Make a drawing of the Colt car badge on a
   piece of A4 5 mm squared paper.
b) At present the registration number on cars end
   in a letter e.g. cars registered between August
   1st, 1981, and July 31st, 1982, all end in the
   letter X. What do you think will happen when
   the end of the alphabet is reached? See if you
   can devise a system for car registration
   numbers when the present system finishes.
   Make a drawing of the type of number plate
   you think will be used in the future.
c) Using a grid of 15 mm squares to help you
   make a copy of the drawing of a Colt
   Sapporo.

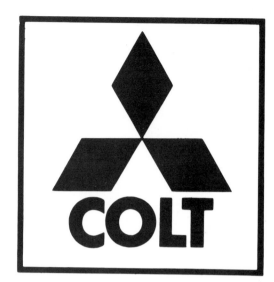

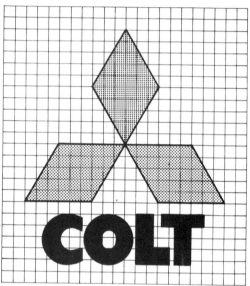

 Red

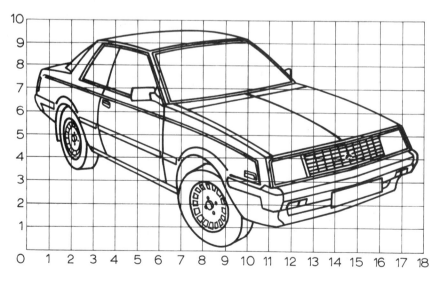

Colt Sapporo

How do you think you can represent the lights?
How can you make the wheels appear more 3D?

42: Television companies

Draw the two television company designs shown
a) London Weekend Television
b) Yorkshire Television
Four quarter elipses have been used to produce
this drawing. What does the Yorkshire Television
symbol suggest to you?

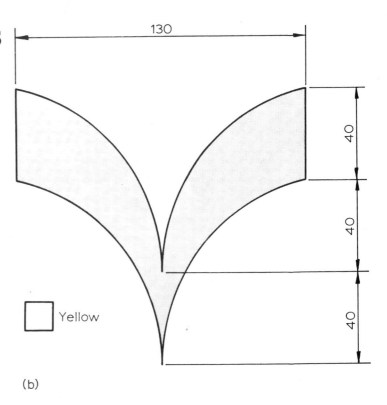

130

40

40

40

☐ Yellow

(b)

☐ Blue

☐ Red

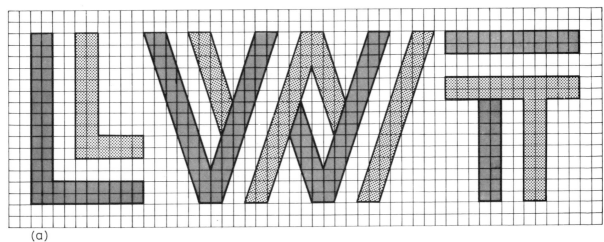

(a)

43: James Bond

The drawing shown here is based around the famous creation of Ian Fleming's JAMES BOND 007. What does the 007 after his name mean? The drawing shows how the 007 has been extended into a gun shape. Make a drawing of this design.

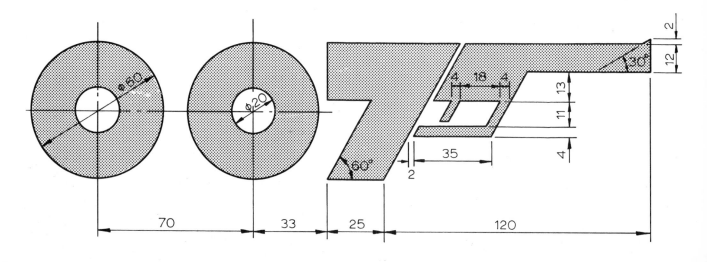

Index

British Library Cataloguing in Publication Data

Rolfe, John
  Design drawing three.
  1. Technical drawings.   2. Mechanical drawing
  I. Title
  604.2'4   T353

ISBN 0 340 26900 6

First printed 1983

Printed in Hong Kong for Hodder and Stoughton Educational,
a division of Hodder and Stoughton Ltd., Mill Road, Dunton
Green, Sevenoaks, Kent TN13 2YD, by Colorcraft Ltd.